Other books by
Carmen & Rosemary Martínez Jover

Purchase at:
www.amazon.com & www.carmenmartinezjover.com

I want to have a child,
Whatever it takes!

Somy's Search

Recipes of How
Babies are Made

A tiny itsy bitsy gift of life,
an egg donor story: girls*

A tiny itsy bitsy gift of life,
an egg donor story: boys*

The Twin Kangaroo
Treasure Hunt*

Available in:
English, Español, Français, Italiano,
Português, Svenska, Türkiye, Česky, Русский & Nederlands

We dedicate this book
to all those who strive to reach for
the **treasures in their lives.**

Carmen & Rosemary Martinez Jover

Text copyright © 2009 Carmen Martinez Jover
www.carmenmartinezjover.com
illustrations copyright © 2009 Rosemary Martinez
www.rmartdesign.com

ISBN 978-607-00-0846-7

The Baby Kangaroo Treasure Hunt
1st edition, June 2009
2nd edition, June 2011

Story: Carmen Martinez Jover
Design & illustrations: Rosemary Martinez
Layout: Victor Alfonso Nieto
Skecthes: Rosemary Martinez & Judith Ferado

For completing your family through Gestational Surrogacy &
Donor Egg IVF contact rotundachr@gmail.com. Read more
about the LGBT friendly clinic at www.iwannagetpregnant.com
Special thanks to www.endometriosis.org,
www.ami-ac.com & sisab.net

The Baby Kangaroo Treasure Hunt

Written by

Carmen Martinez Jover

Illustrated by

Rosemary Martinez

There were once
two kangaroos:
Jack and Sam.

They lived very happily
in their cosy little home.

One day, while they were having an
ice cream at the fair and watching all the
little kangaroos playing around them,
Sam said, "Jack, wouldn't it be lovely to
have our own baby kangaroo?"

Jack smiled and replied,
"Yes. Let's go and visit Wise William
so he can give us some advice."

"Hello, Wise William,"
said Jack and Sam.

"What a lovely surprise to see you!"
replied Wise William,
"What may I do for you?"

"We need your advice. You see...
We want to have our own
baby kangaroo and
we don't know where to start,"
they said.

"Wonderful!
I have just what you need.
Let me see…"
he said, as he searched in
his old treasure trunk.

"The Baby Kangaroo
Treasure Hunt!"

"On this there is a list
of things you need
to have your own baby kangaroo.
Once you discover where
to get them all,
come back and I will tell you
what to do next."

12

Jack and Sam read
the curled scroll containing
The Baby Kangaroo Treasure Hunt
very carefully.

"Ok, the first thing on
the list is a sperm,"
said Jack.

"We both have sperm,
but it doesn't really
matter whose sperm
we use, the baby will be
both of ours anyway,"
said Sam.

16

"We can use your sperm or use mine," said Jack.

"I am so excited soon we will both be Dads," said Sam.

Jack and Sam happily ticked off
the first item on the list that
Wise William had given them.

"Now we need to find an egg,"
said Jack.

"Let's go and visit Kind Kamila!"
said Sam.

18

"Hello, Kind Kamila,"
said Jack and Sam.

"What a lovely surprise to see you!"
replied Kind Kamila,
"What may I do for you?"

"We need your help. You see, we want to have our own baby kangaroo and we were wondering if you would let us have one of your eggs," they said.

"Oh, yes of course!" said Kind Kamila with a smile, "I have lots of them and would love to give you one, which means that I would be an egg donor and will help you have your own baby kangaroo."

Very early next morning,
Jack and Sam went to visit
Sweet Susan to ask her if she would
lend her pouch for a few months so
that their baby kangaroo
could grow inside her.

"Oh, yes of course!"
said Sweet Susan with a smile,
"I would love to lend you my pouch
for a few months, which means that
I would be a surrogate mother
for your baby kangaroo."

Jack and Sam were very excited that they had found everything listed on **The Baby Kangaroo Treasure Hunt** scroll and immediately went to visit Wise William again to see what they had to do next.

Wise William congratulated them for having completed the first part of the list so quickly.

"Now you need..." said Wise William, while Jack and Sam listened very carefully, "Now you need to go with Dr. Good Gotunda who knows how to bring together everything on **The Baby Kangaroo Treasure Hunt** list".

"Please promise to visit me when your baby kangaroo is born," he said enthusiastically.

In the clinic, Dr. Good Gotunda gently put
Kind Kamila's egg and Jack's sperm together in a
test tube and patiently looked after them until
they fertilized and became one, forming an embryo,
which is the beginning of a baby.

When the embryo started to grow,
Dr. Good Gotunda placed it
into Sweet Susan's womb,
hidden in her pouch,
where it continued...

to grow...
and grow...
and grow.

A few months later Sweet Susan gave birth to Jack and Sam's baby kangaroo.

At last, Jack and Sam
went to visit Wise William.

Now they were a very
happy family, with baby Joey,
their much desired treasure.

CPSIA information can be obtained
at www.ICGtesting.com
Printed in the USA
BVHW020102170921
616834BV00002B/106